MORTEN LAURIDSE

Lux aeterna

SATB *divisi*
with chamber orchestra or organ

p13.

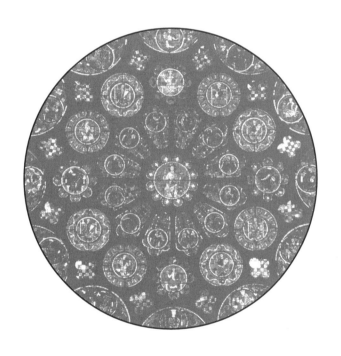

VOCAL SCORE

FABER *ff* MUSIC

Music © copyright 1997 by Southern Music Publishing Co., Inc.
This edition first published in 2002 by Faber Music Ltd as exclusive licencee
in UK, Eire, Australia, New Zealand, Hong Kong, Singapore, Malaysia and South Africa
3 Queen Square London WC1N 3AU
Cover: 12th-century rose window, Chartres Cathedral
Printed in England by Caligraving Ltd

ISBN 0-571-52154-1

The orchestral version of *Lux aeterna* is recorded by the Los Angeles Master Chorale,
conducted by Paul Salamunovich, on RCM (19705).
The organ version is recorded by the Nordic Chamber Choir,
conducted by Nicol Matt, on Bayer (100305).

Lux aeterna was commissioned by the Board of Governors of The Music Center, Inc.,
in honour of Shelton g. Stanfill.

To buy Faber Music publications or to find out about the full range of titles available
please contact your local music retailer or Faber Music sales enquiries:

Faber Music Limited, Burnt Mill, Elizabeth Way, Harlow, CM20 2HX England
Tel: +44 (0)1279 82 89 82 Fax: +44 (0)1279 82 89 83
sales@fabermusic.com fabermusic.com

PREFACE

LUX AETERNA for chorus and chamber orchestra was composed for and is dedicated to the Los Angeles Master Chorale and its superb conductor, Paul Salamunovich, who gave the world premiere in the Dorothy Chandler Pavilion on 13 April, 1997. Each of the five connected movements in this cycle contains references to Light assembled from various sacred Latin texts. The piece opens and closes with the beginning and ending of the Requiem Mass, with the central three movements drawn respectively from the *Te Deum* (including a line from the *Beatus vir*), *O nata lux*, and *Veni, Sancte Spiritus*.

The instrumental introduction to the **Introitus** softly recalls motivic fragments from two pieces especially close to my heart (my settings of Rilke's 'Contre qui, rose' from *Les chansons des roses* and of *O magnum mysterium*), which recur throughout the work in various forms. Several new themes in the **Introitus** are then introduced by the chorus, including an extended canon on 'et lux perpetua'. In te, Domine, speravi contains, among other musical elements, the cantus firmus 'Herzliebster Jesu' (from the *Nuremberg Songbook*, 1677) and a lengthy inverted canon on 'Fiat misericordia'. **O nata lux** and **Veni, Sancte Spiritus** are paired songs, the former a central, a cappella motet and the latter a spirited, jubilant canticle. A quiet setting of the **Agnus Dei** precedes the final **Lux aeterna**, which reprises the opening section of the **Introitus** and concludes with a joyful 'Alleluia'.

The chorus/organ version of *Lux aeterna* was jointly premiered the weekend of 26–27 April, 1997 in Portland by Oregon's celebrated chamber chorus, Choral Cross-Ties, conducted by Bruce Browne, and by the Los Angeles Master Chorale at Loyola Marymount University in Los Angeles. I would like especially to express my gratitude to organist James Paul Buonemani of St. James' Episcopal Church, Los Angeles, for his invaluable assistance in realizing the organ score.

MORTEN LAURIDSEN
Composer-in-Residence, Los Angeles Master Chorale

ORCHESTRA

Flute

Oboe

Clarinet in A

Bassoon

2 Horns in F

Bass Trombone
or Trombone with F attachment

Strings
The string complement at the premiere performance for the 120-voice Los Angeles Master Chorale was 12-10-8-6-4. A reduced string section (10-8-6-5-3 or 8-6-5-4-2) may be used with smaller choruses.

Orchestral material available on hire from the publishers

Duration: *c.*27 minutes

LUX AETERNA

I Introitus *page 1*

Requiem aeternam	*Rest eternal*
dona eis, Domine:	*give to them, Lord:*
et lux perpetua luceat eis.	*and let light perpetual shine on them.*
Te decet hymnus Deus in Zion,	*A hymn befits you, God, in Zion,*
et tibi reddetur votum	*and to you shall be fulfilled a promise*
in Jerusalem:	*in Jerusalem:*
exaudi orationem meam,	*hear my prayer,*
ad te omnis caro veniet.	*to you all flesh shall come.*
Requiem aeternam	*Rest eternal*
dona eis, Domine:	*give to them, Lord:*
et lux perpetua luceat eis.	*and let light perpetual shine on them.*

II In te, Domine, speravi *page 13*

Tu ad liberandum	*To deliver us,*
suscepturus hominem	*you became man,*
non horruisti Virginis uterum.	*not disdaining the Virgin's womb.*
Tu devicto mortis aculeo,	*With the sting of death vanquished,*
aperuisti credentibus	*you opened to believers*
regna coelorum.	*the kingdoms of heaven.*
Exortum est in tenebris	*There is risen in the shadows*
lumen rectis.	*a light for the righteous.*
Miserere nostri, Domine,	*Have mercy on us, Lord,*
miserere nostri.	*have mercy on us.*
Fiat misericordia tua, Domine,	*Let your mercy, Lord,*
super nos,	*be upon us*
quemadmodum speravimus in te.	*inasmuch as we have trusted in you.*
In te, Domine, speravi:	*In you, Lord, I have trusted:*
non confundar in aeternum.	*let me never be confounded.*

III O nata lux *page 20*

O nata lux de lumine,	*Born light from light,*
Jesu redemptor saeculi,	*Jesus, redeemer of the age,*
Dignare clemens supplicum	*mercifully deign to accept suppliants'*
Laudes precesque sumere.	*praises and prayers.*
Qui carne quondam contegi	*You once deigned to take on flesh*
Dignatus es pro perditis.	*for the sake of the lost damned.*
Nos membra confer effici,	*Grant that we be made members*
Tui beati corporis.	*of your blessed body.*

IV Veni, Sancte Spiritus *page 26*

Veni, Sancte Spiritus,	*Come, Holy Spirit,*
Et emitte coelitus	*and send from heaven*
Lucis tuae radium.	*the ray of your light.*
Veni, pater pauperum,	*Come, father of paupers,*
Veni, dator munerum,	*come, donor of gifts,*
Veni, lumen cordium.	*come, light of hearts.*

Consolator optime,	*Best of consolers,*
Dulcis hospes animae,	*sweet host of the soul,*
Dulce refrigerium.	*sweet respite.*
In labore requies,	*Amid labour, rest,*
In aestu temperies,	*amid heat, moderation,*
In fletu solatium.	*amid tears, solace.*
O lux beatissima,	*Light most blessed,*
Reple cordis intima	*fill the inmost parts of the heart*
Tuorum fidelium.	*of your faithful.*
Sine tuo numine,	*Without your spirit,*
Nihil est in homine,	*there is nothing in man,*
Nihil est innoxium.	*nothing harmless.*
Lava quod est sordidum,	*Clean what is dirty,*
Riga quod est aridum,	*moisten what is dry,*
Sana quod est saucium.	*heal what is wounded.*
Flecte quod est rigidum,	*Bend what is rigid,*
Fove quod est frigidum,	*warm what is cold,*
Rege quod est devium.	*guide what is straying.*
Da tuis fidelibus,	*Give to your faithful,*
In te confidentibus,	*those trusting in you,*
Sacrum septenarium.	*sacred seven-fold gifts.*
Da virtutis meritum,	*Give the reward of virtue,*
Da salutis exitum,	*give the deliverance of salvation,*
Da perenne gaudium.	*give eternal joy.*

V Agnus Dei – Lux aeterna *page 35*

Agnus Dei,	*Lamb of God,*
qui tollis peccata mundi,	*who takes away the sins of the world,*
dona eis requiem.	*give them rest.*
Agnus Dei,	*Lamb of God,*
qui tollis peccata mundi,	*who takes away the sins of the world,*
dona eis requiem.	*give them rest.*
Agnus Dei,	*Lamb of God,*
qui tollis peccata mundi,	*who takes away the sins of the world,*
dona eis requiem sempiternam.	*give them rest everlasting.*
Lux aeterna luceat eis, Domine:	*Let light eternal shine on them, Lord:*
cum sanctis tuis in aeternum:	*in the company of your saints for ever:*
quia pius es.	*for you are merciful.*
Requiem aeternam	*Rest eternal*
dona eis, Domine:	*give to them, Lord:*
et lux perpetua luceat eis.	*and let light perpetual shine on them.*
Alleluia. Amen.	*Alleluia. Amen.*

Lux aeterna

I Introitus

Morten Lauridsen
(1997)

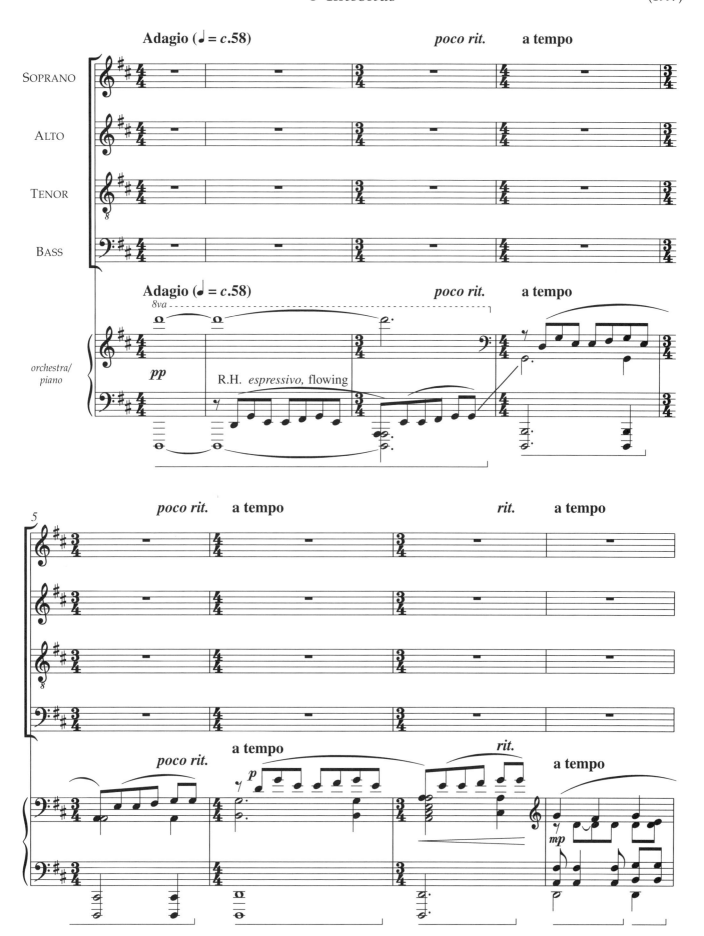

2

A

Re-qui-em ae-ter-nam   do-na e-is, Do-mi-ne.

Re-qui-em ae-ter-nam   do-na e-is, Do-mi-ne.

Re-qui-em ae-ter-nam   do-na e-is, Do-mi-ne.

A

Re-qui-em ae-ter-nam   do-na e-is, Do-mi-ne.

*The single instrumental line from bar 98 to 106 is to be played (by solo cello) only in the orchestral version and in rehearsal. Do not play this line in either organ or piano performances.

II In te, Domine, speravi

* Cantus Firmus, 'Herzliebster Jesu', *Nuremberg Songbook*, 1677

non hor-ru-is-sti Vir-gin-is u-te-rum.

non hor-ru-i-sti Vir-gin-is u-te-rum.

III O nata lux

When performing with piano, only the low 'D' octave of the first bar is to be played.
The remainder of *O nata lux* is a cappella; the written piano part is for rehearsal only.

IV Veni, Sancte Spiritus

28

V Agnus Dei – Lux aeterna

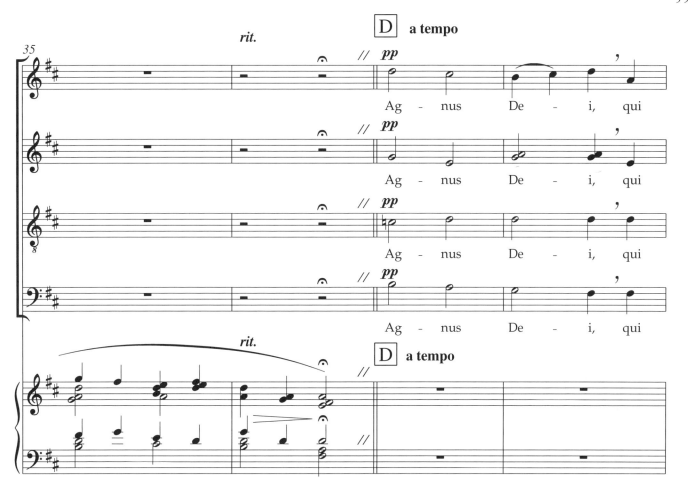